LONGM

Round the World in Eighty Days

Jules Verne

Simplified by D K Swan
Illustrated by Robert Geary

Longman

Longman Group UK Limited,
Longman House, Burnt Mill, Harlow,
Essex CM20 2JE, England
and Associated Companies throughout the world.

This simplified edition © Longman Group UK Limited 1991

First published in 1991
Second impression 1991

ISBN 0-582-01817-X

Set in 12/14 point Linotron 202 Versailles
Produced by Longman Group (FE) Limited
Printed in Hong Kong

Acknowledgements

The cover background is a wallpaper design called NUAGE,
courtesy of Osborne and Little plc.

Stage 2: 900 word vocabulary

Please look under *New words* at the back of this book
for explanations of words outside this stage.

Contents

Introduction

Jules Verne

The writer Jules Verne was born at Nantes, in the west of France, in 1828. Most of Jules Verne's stories told the readers about very many things that were going to be used or discovered or invented in the future.

As a young man, Jules Verne studied law, but he began writing plays for the theatre. In 1862, he wrote a novel, *Cinq semaines en ballon* (Five Weeks in a Balloon). It showed that Jules Verne could make imaginary journeys exciting. And it was the first of the novels that have given Verne the name of the "father of science fiction". It was an immediate success in France. People in other countries heard about it, and Verne's French novel was translated – into English, for example, in 1869.

Round the World in Eighty Days appeared in French in 1873. By this time, Verne's novels were known in very many countries; this one appeared in English and other languages in the same year, 1873. It was not a story about possible ways of travelling in the future, but about the latest forms of travel in 1872. And you will find fun in it, too.

The science fiction stories of Jules Verne are still popular. Readers have certainly met one or more of them in film or on television. The success of his books made it possible for him to buy a fishing-boat on which he sailed and wrote. As he became more successful, he bought bigger boats and sailed longer distances. All the time, the books poured from his pen.

It was only when he lost his eyesight in 1902 that Jules Verne stopped writing and sailing. He died in 1905.

The date
When you travel *east* round the world, you put the clock forward one hour for each 15° of longitude. Your clock then shows the right time for the "time zone" you have entered. (The time zones were agreed in 1918.) When you have done this twelve times, you have reached longitude 180° and the "international date line". This imaginary line was agreed in 1884 (after Jules Verne's book was written). Today when you cross the international date line, travelling east, you repeat one day.

For example, suppose you are crossing the Pacific Ocean from Japan to America. On 23rd November, your ship (or plane) crosses the international date line. The ship's (or plane's) officers will tell you to call the day 22nd November. Tomorrow you will start 23rd November again. You have gained a day.

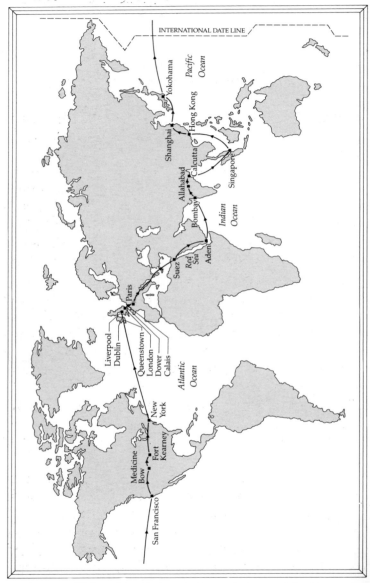

Phileas Fogg's journey round the world

Chapter 1
Phileas Fogg and Passepartout

Phileas Fogg lived at 7 Savile Row, but he spent most of his time at the Reform Club in London's Pall Mall.

He was a silent man. Nobody knew much about him. He left his house at 11.30 every morning to walk to the club, and he left the club in time to walk back to Savile Row and go to bed at midnight. He had his lunch and his dinner at the club. He read the papers there, and he played the card game called whist.

Phileas Fogg was also an exact man. He expected his one manservant to be exact, too. Forster, his last manservant, had not been exact enough, and he had gone. Phileas Fogg was waiting at his Savile Row house for the man who was to take Forster's place.

The man who arrived was about thirty years old.

"You are French," said Phileas Fogg, "and your name is John?"

"Jean, if you don't mind, sir. Jean Passepartout, they call me, because I used to be good at getting out of trouble. I am a good man, sir, but I have done a lot of different kinds of work. At one time I worked in a circus, riding, jumping, walking the tightrope. Then I became a teacher of gymnastics. After that, I was a fireman in

1

Paris. But I left France five years ago, and I came to England to find a quiet life as a manservant. I heard that you were the quietest man in Britain, and I would like to work for you because I want to live quietly and forget the name Passepartout."

"I'll call you Passepartout," said Phileas Fogg. "What time is it?"

Passepartout pulled a big silver watch from his pocket. "It is 11.29, sir," he said.

"All right. From now, 11.29 on 2nd October 1872, I am your employer."

With those words, Phileas Fogg put on his hat, and went out. Passepartout was left in the house alone.

"Well, here I am," the Frenchman said to himself. "But what do I do?"

He went into all the rooms in the house. One of them was clearly his own room, and in it he found a timetable of the things he must do. Everything was there, from 8 o'clock, when Phileas Fogg got up, to 11.30, when he left the house to go to the Reform Club: tea at 8.23; shaving water (31°C) at 9.37, etc. Then from 11.30 in the morning until exactly midnight, when the gentleman always went to bed, everything was clearly written down.

Passepartout smiled. "This is just right for me," he thought. "Mr Fogg and I are going to understand each other! He likes to live like a clock. He *is* a clock."

Phileas Fogg asks Passepartout the time

Chapter 2
The bet

At the Reform Club, Phileas Fogg had his meals at exactly the usual times. He read *The Times* in his usual chair at the usual times.

At 6.10, the five gentlemen who always played whist with Phileas Fogg took their places in the card room, and he joined them.

Whist is the most silent of card games. But this evening, before the game started the gentlemen spoke about a thief. The papers said that this man had stolen fifty-five thousand pounds from the Bank of England. One of the whist players was a governor of the Bank of England.

"They'll catch the man," he said. "The best detectives have been sent to every port. They have an exact description of the gentleman."

"A description? A gentleman?"

"Yes," said Ralph, the bank governor. "Nobody saw him take the fifty-five thousand pounds, but a number of people saw a stranger in the room the banknotes were taken from. He was well dressed, tall, good-looking – a real gentleman. He won't escape."

"Oh, I don't know," said Stuart. "The world is a very big place."

"It *was* a big place," said Phileas Fogg.

"How do you mean – 'was'? Has it become smaller?"

"Yes," said Ralph. "I think Mr Fogg is right. You can go round the world ten times more quickly than a hundred years ago."

"All right," said Stuart. "But just because you can go round the world in about three months——"

"In eighty days," said Phileas Fogg.

"Fogg's right," said Ralph. "The part of the railway between Rothal and Allahabad is open now, so *The Times* has worked out this time-table." And he showed them, on the centre page of the paper:

London to Suez – rail and ship	7 days
Suez to Bombay – ship	13
Bombay to Calcutta – railway	3
Calcutta to Hong Kong – ship	13
Hong Kong to Yokohama – ship	6
Yokohama to San Francisco – ship	22
San Francisco to New York – railway	7
New York to London – ship and rail	9
	80 days

"Yes," said Stuart, "eighty days. But that doesn't allow anything for storms, accidents, attack by enemies ..."

"It allows for everything," Phileas Fogg answered.

"It's all right on paper," said Stuart. "But in real life ..."

"In real life too, Mr Stuart."

"I'd like to see you try, Mr Fogg."

"Well, let's *all* go. Then you *will* see me."

"No, thank you," said Stuart. "But I'll bet four thousand pounds that the journey can't be done in the time."

"It can," Phileas Fogg said.

"Well, do it!"

"Go round the world in eighty days? All right."

Phileas Fogg's friends were surprised. They were even more surprised when he said: "I have twenty thousand pounds in Baring's Bank. I'm ready to bet that amount that I can do it."

"Twenty thousand pounds!" cried Ralph. "Twenty thousand pounds that an unexpected delay can cause you to lose?"

"Nothing is ever unexpected," Fogg said.

In the end, Phileas Fogg's five friends took the bet. If he made the journey round the world in eighty days, or less, they would pay him twenty thousand pounds. If the journey took more than eighty days, he would pay them that amount – four thousand pounds each.

"Right," said Fogg. "The train for Dover leaves at 8.45 this evening. I'll be on it."

Fogg looked at his pocket book. "Today is Wednesday 2nd October. So I must be back here, in this room in the Reform Club, on Saturday 21st December at 8.45 in the evening."

At 7.25, Phileas Fogg said good night to his friends and left the Reform Club. At 7.50, he opened the door of his own house and went in.

Passepartout had read his timetable very carefully. He was surprised to see Mr Fogg. His timetable told him to expect his employer at midnight exactly.

Phileas Fogg called him. "We leave in ten minutes for Dover and Calais," he said. "We are going round the world."

Passepartout's eyes opened wide – very wide. His arms reached far out. He was a picture of surprise.

"Round the world!" he breathed.

"In eighty days," said Phileas Fogg. "We mustn't waste a minute."

"But your baggage?"

"No baggage. Just one overnight bag. Two shirts and some socks. The same for you. We can buy things on the way. Bring down my overcoat. Wear strong shoes. Move!"

At 8 o'clock, Passepartout was ready with a small bag holding clothes for his employer and himself. He left his room, closing the door carefully. His thoughts were going round and round. "A quiet life," he said. "A quiet life!"

Mr Fogg was ready. He had a book under his arm, *Bradshaw's World Railway and Steamship Guide*. He took the bag from Passepartout and put into it a very thick roll of banknotes. Then he passed the bag to Passepartout. "Look after it," he said. "There's twenty thousand pounds in it."

Passepartout nearly dropped the bag.

At the station, Phileas Fogg saw his five friends from the Reform Club.

"You are kind to come to say goodbye," he said. "I'll have stamps in my passport to show where I have been, and you can see them when I come back."

"That's not necessary," said Ralph. "We'll take your word as a gentleman."

At 8.40, Phileas Fogg and Passepartout took their places in the train, and at 8.45 the train started.

The story of the bet, and Phileas Fogg's plan to go round the world in eighty days, were the talk of London. The story was in every newspaper the next day and for the following week. There were a lot of bets on the result.

Then the chief of the London police received a telegram:

> Suez 9 October
> To Chief of Police, Scotland Yard, London.
> Am following bank thief Phileas Fogg. Send warrant without delay to Bombay.
> *Fix (detective)*

That was exciting. "Was Phileas Fogg really the thief?" the papers asked. People remembered the surprising story of the bet. "Was it just to hide the true reason for the journey?" *The Times* wrote.

Chapter 3
Detective Fix

On Wednesday 9th October, the passenger steamer *Mongolia* was expected at Suez after passing through the Suez Canal. She was one of the fastest ships of the P. & O. steamship company.

One of the people who were waiting for the ship at Suez was a small, thin man with very bright eyes. His name was Fix, and he was one of the detectives who had been sent by Scotland Yard to different ports to watch for the bank thief. His orders were to look at every passenger travelling through Suez. He had read the description of the "gentleman-thief". If he saw someone who might be the thief, he had to follow him until the warrant arrived for the man's arrest.

The *Mongolia* arrived in the port, and Phileas Fogg went to get a stamp in his passport. Then he went straight back to the ship. Fix watched him. Then the detective found Passepartout still on land, looking at the town and the people.

"Can I help you?" asked Fix.

"You're very kind," said Passepartout. "This is Suez, is it?"

"Yes. Suez."

"In Egypt?"

"Yes. In Egypt."

"In Africa?"

"Yes."

Passepartout said, "It's hard to believe it. I hoped to stay for a time in Paris, but I saw Paris only from 7.20 in the morning until 8.15, through the windows of a carriage, between two railway stations. And now here I am in Africa."

"You're in a hurry, then?" asked the detective.

"No, I'm not. My employer is. Oh, and I have to buy some shirts. We came away without baggage – just an overnight bag. So we need some more clothes."

"I'll show you the way to the shops."

"Thank you," said Passepartout. And the two men started walking. "I must be careful not to miss the boat," the Frenchman said.

"You've got plenty of time," Fix answered. "It isn't twelve o'clock yet."

Passepartout pulled out his big watch. "Twelve?" he said. "It's 9.52!"

"Your watch is slow."

"My watch? Slow? It's a very fine old family watch. It doesn't lose five minutes in a whole year. It keeps wonderful time!"

"Ah! I see," said Fix. "You've still got London time, and that is two hours behind Suez time. You must change your watch to show the time of each country you go to."

"What! Change my watch? Never!"

"Then the time by your watch won't be the same as the sun's time."

"Well, sir," said Passepartout, "the sun will be wrong!"

A few minutes later, Fix said, "Here are the shops. You can buy everything you need here. – You left London in a hurry, did you?"

"We certainly did. Last Wednesday, Mr Fogg came back from his club at eight in the evening – a thing he never did – and three-quarters of an hour later we had started."

Fix thought about that. Then he asked, "But where is your employer going?"

"Round the world."

"Round the world?"

"Yes, in eighty days. He says it's for a bet."

"Is he rich?" Fix wanted to know.

"He seems rich," said Passepartout, always ready to talk about anything. "He's got a lot of new banknotes with him, and he spends them freely. I know he has promised to give the chief engineer of the *Mongolia* a lot of money if we reach Bombay early."

And that is why the detective sent the telegram to London. He had seen Phileas Fogg, who was just like the description of the bank thief. And he had learnt a lot from the talkative Passepartout.

Just before the *Mongolia* left Suez, Fix was on the ship with a light bag and plenty of money.

11

Chapter 4
India

The *Mongolia* travelled quickly through the Red Sea, while Phileas Fogg ate four meals a day and played whist. The ship reached Aden fifteen hours early and stopped there for coal. Phileas Fogg went into the town only to get a stamp in his passport.

In the Indian Ocean, the wind from the north-west allowed the ship to use her sails as well as her engines. The *Mongolia* was expected to arrive in Bombay on 22nd October. She arrived on 20th. Phileas Fogg was two days early. He wrote down the fact in his notebook, but he did not show any joy or excitement.

It was 4.30 in the afternoon when the passengers left the ship. The train from Bombay to Calcutta was to leave at 8 o'clock.

Phileas Fogg gave Passepartout some orders and told him to be at the railway station before 8 o'clock. He himself went to the passport office and then to the station, where he had dinner.

Fix went straight to the Bombay chief of police. He asked about the warrant for the arrest of Phileas Fogg. It had not arrived. The Bombay police could not get a warrant, and they could not arrest Fogg.

Passepartout bought the things that his employer wanted. Then he went to look at

The Mongolia *arrives in Bombay*

Bombay. Everything was interesting to the young man. He liked the look of the fine temple on Malabar Hill, and he went inside.

There was something Passepartout did not know: nobody is allowed to go into a temple wearing shoes. He was looking at some of the beautiful things there when suddenly three men attacked him. They threw him to the floor, and pulled off his shoes. They were priests of the temple, and very angry. They shouted out, and a crowd began to gather. The Frenchman, young and strong, threw the priests to one side, and ran into the street.

At 7.55, just before the train left, Passepartout arrived at the station, without shoes, without a hat, and without the things he had bought.

Fix had followed Phileas Fogg to the station. He hid and listened while Passepartout told his employer what had happened. The detective was going to get into another carriage of the train when a thought made him stop.

"No," he told himself. "One of them has done wrong in this country. I can use that fact to delay the thief until the warrant comes."

The train ran on through the night, and all the next day and the following night. It went through countryside of many kinds. Passepartout watched the many changes through the window. It was all interesting to him. Phileas Fogg seemed not to find it interesting at all.

At 8 o'clock in the morning, on 22nd October, a few kilometres beyond the station of Rothal, the train stopped.

A railwayman came to the carriage window. "All passengers must get out here," he called.

Phileas Fogg asked, "Where are we?"

The railwayman answered: "At the village of Kholby."

"Why have we stopped?"

"The railway line isn't finished. The line begins again at Allahabad, about eighty kilometres from here."

"The papers said the line was finished."

"The papers were wrong, sir."

"But your company sells tickets from Bombay to Calcutta," the Englishman said.

"Oh, yes," the railwayman answered. "But all the passengers know that they have to get from Kholby to Allahabad by other ways."

Passepartout could have hit the railwayman, but Phileas Fogg did not seem excited. "A ship leaves Calcutta for Hong Kong on 25th at 12 o'clock. Today is only 22nd, so we can reach Calcutta in time."

But the other passengers – the passengers who knew all about the line – had left the train quickly, and they had taken all the carriages, carts, horses – everything from the village that could carry them to Allahabad.

"I'll walk," said Phileas Fogg.

Passepartout looked down at his shoeless

feet. "There's an elephant over there," he said.

The elephant's owner hoped to become a rich man. Fogg offered ten pounds an hour. No. Twenty? No. Forty? No.

In the end, the owner sold the elephant to Fogg for two thousand pounds.

"Elephant meat costs a lot," Passepartout thought.

The next thing was to find a guide – a man to show them the way to Allahabad. That was easier: a young Indian who spoke English offered to help them.

Every two hours the guide stopped the elephant and allowed it to rest and to eat and drink. Then they started again, moving quickly. By 8 o'clock in the evening, they had climbed over the Vindhia mountains. They were half-way to Allahabad. The guide stopped for the night.

They started again at 6 o'clock the next morning, and by 4 o'clock in the afternoon they were only a few kilometres from Allahabad. They were in thick forest when suddenly the elephant stopped.

There was a noise of singing and loud music. The guide drove the elephant into a place where the trees and plants grew thickly.

"It's a dead man," he said. "They're taking the body to a temple to burn it."

Through the branches, they saw a crowd passing: first priests, then men playing music, and a crowd of men, women and children. After the crowd there were some men pulling and pushing a young woman. She was very beautiful, but she was very weak; she could only just walk. Then came men carrying the body of an old man in fine clothes.

"It's a prince," said the guide. "The young woman was his wife, and they will burn her with his body. Sometimes a wife will go willingly to her death when her husband dies. But this young girl is not going willingly. They are forcing her to die with the old man."

"Poor girl!" said Passepartout. "But why isn't she trying to get away?"

"They have given her a drug," the guide said.

"We'll save her." They were Phileas Fogg's words, and the guide and Passepartout were surprised. "I am still one day early. We can use the day to save the young lady."

"My employer has a kind heart," Passepartout thought, "even if he usually hides it."

"We can follow them, but we mustn't go too near yet," the guide said. "I know where they are going. It's a temple about three kilometres from here. I know about the young wife, too. She is the daughter of a rich Bombay business man. Her name is Aouda. Her father and mother died, and against her wishes, her family married her to the old prince. I'll help you, but we can't do anything until it's dark."

Chapter 5
Aouda

The guide stopped the elephant a few hundred metres from the temple, and they went quietly towards a great noise of shouting and singing.

It was clear that the girl was inside the temple. It was also clear that men with swords and guns all round the temple were awake. The old prince's body was already on the top of a large pile of wood, waiting to be burnt at sunrise.

"We'll have to wait for a chance to save the young lady," said Phileas Fogg.

From behind some trees and thick bushes, Fogg and the guide watched and waited for that chance. The chance did not come. The men with swords watched the temple all night.

Passepartout had moved away alone.

At the first light of day, the people woke and went noisily towards the place of burning. Phileas Fogg was just behind them. He saw the men bring Aouda out. She had been drugged again, and she did nothing as they laid her down on top of the wood beside the prince's body.

Some men brought fire to the wood. Phileas Fogg started forward ...

Suddenly everything changed. The crowd gave a great cry, and all the people fell down on their faces in fear and surprise.

It seemed that the old prince was not dead. He stood up, picked up the young woman, and came down off the already burning wood pile.

He passed through the crowd, all face-down on the ground. And, carrying the young woman quite easily, came towards Phileas Fogg and the guide.

"Come on!" he said. "Quickly!"

It was Passepartout.

A minute later, the three men and the young woman were on the elephant and it was moving – almost running – through the forest.

Aouda, still drugged, knew nothing about her escape.

Just before 10 o'clock in the morning, the guide said, "There, that is Allahabad. The railway line starts again there, and trains reach Calcutta in less than a day and a night."

Phileas Fogg took a room at the railway station for Aouda. He sent Passepartout into the town to buy clothes and other things for the young lady.

By the time the train was to start, Aouda was better and could take her place in the railway carriage.

Phileas Fogg paid the guide the exact amount he had promised. "That's your pay as a guide," he said. "But you have been a brave man, and you have helped us in other ways. Would you like the elephant?"

The three men and Aouda on the elephant

On the journey to Calcutta, Aouda learnt about her escape. She thanked Phileas Fogg with tears in her eyes. He saw that she was still afraid because the prince's people would follow her to any part of India.

"I'll take you to Hong Kong," he said, "and you can stay there until the matter is forgotten." It was a kind offer, but he made it quite coldly.

She happily said, "Oh, thank you! I have an uncle in Hong Kong. He will look after me." Her English was very good. She had been at an English school in Bombay, and it was a pleasure to hear her speak.

The train reached Calcutta at 7 o'clock in the morning. Phileas Fogg had five hours before the ship was to leave for Hong Kong at 12 o'clock.

Chapter 6
Calcutta

Phileas Fogg was leaving the station to go straight to the passport office and the ship. A policeman came up to him and said:

"Are you Mr Phileas Fogg?"

"Yes, I am."

"And this is your manservant?"

"Yes."

"Please follow me, both of you."

Fogg showed no surprise. "Can this young lady come with us?" he asked.

At the police station they were told: "You will appear in front of Judge Obadiah at 8.30."

When 8.30 came, a policeman led them to a large room where Judge Obadiah was expected.

Three priests came in, and a man held up Passepartout's shoes. Phileas Fogg and Passepartout had forgotten about the trouble in the Bombay temple. They did not see Fix, although he was in the room.

The detective had heard Passepartout at the station at Bombay. He had gone to the priests in the temple on Malabar Hill, and they had got on the train twelve hours later than Fogg's. Because saving the young woman had taken time, Fix and the priests were in Calcutta before Phileas Fogg and Passepartout.

Judge Obadiah came in. He said, "This is

a very serious matter. You must both stay in prison until your trial."

Fix, hidden in his corner of the room, was very happy. "This will give the warrant time to arrive," he told himself.

Passepartout was very unhappy. He did not mind going to prison himself, but it was very bad for his employer. "A bet of twenty thousand pounds lost. And why? Because I foolishly went into a temple in shoes!"

Phileas Fogg's face showed nothing. He stood up and said: "I offer bail."

"Yes, you can do that," said the judge. (Fix felt cold.) "But," Judge Obadiah added, "because you are strangers in this country, I fix the bail at one thousand pounds for each of you." (Fix was pleased. Fogg would lose two thousand pounds if he and Passepartout did not come back for the trial.)

"I'll pay," said Phileas Fogg.

"This money will be given back to you," said the judge, "when you come back for your trial. Just now you are free to go, on bail."

"But they must give me back my shoes, mustn't they?" said Passepartout.

With the Frenchman wearing his shoes again, the travellers hurried out. Fogg, Aouda and Passepartout took a carriage and went straight to the port. Fix followed, very angry.

"If he goes on like this," Fix thought, "he soon won't have any of the stolen money left."

Chapter 7
To Hong Kong

The *Rangoon* was a fast passenger ship. She could make the voyage from Calcutta to Hong Kong in eleven or twelve days.

During the first few days on the ship, Aouda learnt more about Phileas Fogg – but still not a great deal. From a full heart she thanked him for what he had done for her. Her feelings were quite clearly shown. Phileas Fogg, as usual, showed no feelings. He listened politely, but that was all.

Fix was on the ship. He had arranged for the warrant to be sent to Hong Kong, and he had joined the passengers on the *Rangoon* without being seen by Passepartout. When Passepartout did see him on the ship, he was surprised.

"What is Mr Fix doing on this ship?" the Frenchman wondered. "I thought he was in Suez. Is he too going round the world? Is he following us? Why?" He thought about it, and then suddenly it seemed clear. "He *is* following Mr Fogg. He has been sent by those gentlemen at the Reform Club." And Passepartout was angry with them, but he did not tell Phileas Fogg. His employer would be hurt if he knew his friends did not trust him.

On 31st October, early in the morning, the *Rangoon* stopped at Singapore for coal.

The ship was earlier than usual in leaving Singapore, but after that, a strong wind and great waves slowed her down. The delay did not seem to make Phileas Fogg angry, but Passepartout was very angry – with the wind, the sea, the captain, the engineer, the steamship company – because by now he really liked his employer. He wanted him to win his bet, more than he had ever wanted anything.

The *Rangoon* reached Hong Kong twenty-four hours late.

"We have missed the sailing of the *Carnatic* for Yokohama, haven't we?" Fogg asked the port officer.

"No, sir," said the officer. "The *Carnatic* had trouble with one of her engines, so she didn't sail yesterday. She'll leave tomorrow."

"Thank you," said Fogg quietly. His face showed no feelings. But Passepartout shook the officer's hand, and his smile was wide.

Phileas Fogg took Aouda to the best hotel in Hong Kong. Then he went to find her uncle.

An hour later, he came back and asked to speak to the young lady. Her uncle was not in Hong Kong. He had gone to live in Holland.

Aouda did not speak for a minute. She sat with her head in her hands. Then in her soft voice she asked very simply:

"What must I do, Mr Fogg?"

"That's easy," said the gentleman. "You must come to Europe."

25

"But I can't trouble you——"

"It's no trouble. And having you with us won't change my timetable. Passepartout?"

"Yes, sir."

"Go to the *Carnatic*, Passepartout, and pay for three cabins to Yokohama."

Passepartout left the hotel smiling. He was glad Aouda was going with them. She always spoke kindly to him and treated him as a gentleman.

When Passepartout arrived at the part of the port where the *Carnatic* was, he saw a very unhappy-looking Fix.

Fix's warrant had not arrived at Hong Kong, and the *Carnatic* had not yet sailed. Passepartout was pleased. ("The gentlemen of the Reform Club are going to lose their money," the Frenchman thought, "and Mr Fix's costly journey will have been for nothing.")

"Are you coming to get a cabin on the *Carnatic*?" Passepartout laughed.

There were plenty of cabins on the *Carnatic*, and Passepartout paid for three.

The man who took the money for the cabins said, "They've finished mending the engine, so the ship will leave at 8 o'clock this evening. Not tomorrow."

"Good," said Passepartout. "That'll please my employer. I'll go and tell him."

"There's no hurry," said Fix. "Won't you

have a drink with me at this bar?" And he pointed to a bar near the ships.

"Well, yes, thank you. I am quite thirsty," the Frenchman said.

In the bar, Fix asked Passepartout, "Who do you think I am?"

"I know who you are," said Passepartout. "You are working for the men of the Reform Club. You are watching my employer."

"It's true that I am watching your employer," said Fix. "But I am not working for the men of any club. I'm a policeman, and I'm following Mr Fogg because he's a bank thief. You must help me, or you will be arrested too."

"What for?" asked Passepartout. He thought Fix was telling a foolish story, though he remembered it later.

Fix went on talking, but Passepartout understood less and less of what he said. He knew only that Fix was Phileas Fogg's enemy. He tried to stand up. He wanted to hit the detective, but his arms and legs would not obey him.

Fix had put a strong drug into the Frenchman's drink. He wanted to separate the man from his employer. Then Fogg would not know that the ship was going to sail that evening. Passepartout was a healthy man who had never taken any drug or strong drink, so the drug and the drink together worked very quickly to make him fall into a deep sleep. Fix left him in the bar.

Fix asks Passepartout to have a drink with him

Chapter 8
To Japan

In the town, Phileas Fogg took Aouda to the shops. "It's all right," he thought, "for a man to travel with just a small bag. But a lady who is travelling needs quite a lot of things." So they bought dresses and many other things.

Aouda did not know what to say about all the spending, but Phileas Fogg told her that it was quite all right.

"These things are needed for my journey," he said. "They are a part of my plan."

When night came, and Passepartout had not appeared, Fogg asked questions. There were no answers.

In the morning, Passepartout was still not in the hotel. But no one could see what Phileas Fogg thought about that. He sent for a carriage, and he and Aouda set out for the port. He expected to find both the *Carnatic* and his man-servant there. But he was told that the *Carnatic* had sailed the evening before. And Passepartout was not in the port.

An Englishman spoke to Phileas Fogg. "Were you hoping to sail in the *Carnatic*, sir?" It was Fix. "I, too, expected to find the ship here, and I don't know what to do. It seems the *Carnatic* sailed yesterday evening, and now we have to wait a week for the next ship."

Fix looked unhappy, but as he said the words "wait a week", he had joy in his heart. He was sure the warrant for Fogg's arrest would arrive in less than a week. But his joy did not last long. It left him when he heard Fogg say: "But there are other ships in the port of Hong Kong besides the *Carnatic*. Let's go and find one."

Phileas Fogg looked for a ship for a long time. It seemed that they were all loading or unloading. He could not find one that was ready to sail. Then:

"Are you looking for a boat?" asked a voice.

Fogg looked at the seaman who had spoken. "Do you have a boat that is ready to sail?"

"Yes, sir, a pilot-boat. Number 43 – the best in Hong Kong."

"Is it fast?"

"Yes, sir. Ten or eleven kilometres an hour."

"Will you take me to Yokohama? I have missed the *Carnatic*, and I must be in Yokohama on 14th November to catch the ship for San Francisco. I offer you a hundred pounds a day, and two hundred pounds more if I arrive in time."

"But why Yokohama?" said the pilot. "We could sail to Shanghai, only 1,200 kilometres from Hong Kong. The ship for San Francisco sails from Shanghai to Yokohama before it goes on to America."

Phileas Fogg was surprised. "That's not in my *Bradshaw*," he said. "Are you sure?"

"Quite certain."

"And when does the ship leave Shanghai?"

"On 11th November, at seven in the evening. So we have four days. With the wind in the south-east, as it is now, and the sea as it is now, we can get to Shanghai in four days."

"When can we start?" asked Fogg.

"In an hour – time to get food and water."

"Is she your own boat?"

"Yes, sir. My name is Bunsby, and the *Tankadere* is mine."

"Here's two hundred pounds to begin with," said Phileas Fogg. Then, turning to Fix: "Do you want to come with us?" Fogg asked.

"I was going to ask you ..."

"In half an hour, then," said Fogg.

"But that poor boy ..." Aouda was very unhappy about Passepartout.

"I am going to do everything possible for him," said Fogg. And he went with Aouda to the police, the Governor's offices, and the French consul's office. With each of them he left a description of Passepartout and enough money to pay for his voyage back to Europe.

At 3 o'clock, they were on board the *Tankadere*, and the fast-looking pilot-boat set sail.

At first, the wind helped, and the pilot-boat moved fast towards the north-east. Bunsby kept as much sail on her as he dared, and all the next day the *Tankadere* ran on up the Chinese coast.

But in the early morning of the second day, the pilot came to Phileas Fogg. "There's going to be a bad storm," he said. "We call storms of this kind typhoons, and they're dangerous."

It was a very bad storm. The *Tankadere* sailed on, but with only the smallest sail. The pilot-boat was thrown about, and it needed all Bunsby's seamanship to keep her safe. Fix was frightened and very unhappy. Aouda just watched Phileas Fogg. And Phileas Fogg himself? It seemed that the typhoon was just a part of his plan.

The storm grew worse. Bunsby talked to his sailors, and then came to Fogg.

"I think, sir, that we ought to find a safe port on the Chinese coast."

"Yes," said Phileas Fogg.

"All right," said the pilot. "We must just decide which port."

"I only know one." Phileas Fogg spoke quietly but surely. "Shanghai."

It was a wild night. The little pilot-boat was thrown about by huge waves. Aouda was hurt, although Fogg tried to save her, but the brave girl never cried out.

The next day, the storm became less wild, and Bunsby was able to use more and more sail. The pilot-boat sailed fast through the night.

In the morning, the people on board the *Tankadere* could see the coast.

"We're about a hundred and fifty kilometres

from Shanghai," said the pilot. "We ought to be only fifty, but the storm delayed us. I've set every sail, and we *might* be there in time."

But Bunsby had very little hope of the two hundred pounds that Fogg had offered for arriving in time to catch the ship for Yokohama. The ship to San Francisco was to sail that evening.

By 7 o'clock, they were less than five kilometres from Shanghai. Soon they saw the big American ship coming out of the port towards them.

"Too late!" cried the pilot.

Phileas Fogg said simply: "Your flag. Fly it upside down. That means you're in trouble, doesn't it?"

There were two empty cabins on the *Carnatic* as the ship left Hong Kong on 7th November to sail as fast as she could towards Japan. Passepartout was on board the ship.

Fix had left Passepartout in the bar, drugged. The drug ought to have kept him asleep for six hours or more. But after three hours, Passepartout shook himself. He could hardly think, but one word went round and round in the pain that filled his head: *"Carnatic! Carnatic!"* He pulled himself out of the bar. He could see the *Carnatic* from the bar door, and he made himself walk to it. Falling against things, falling down on the ground, falling and getting up again, he reached the ship just before she sailed. On the ship, he fell down for the last time, and he knew nothing more until the next morning.

In the morning, Passepartout breathed the sea air until his head cleared. Then he went to the ship's office and asked for Phileas Fogg's cabin number.

Phileas Fogg was not on board. Aouda was not on the ship. Passepartout sat down. "What has happened?" he wondered.

And then he remembered. He remembered that the ship's sailing time had been changed — that he ought to have told Mr Fogg — that he had not told him. Phileas Fogg and Aouda had missed the ship, and it was his fault.

"My fault!" he thought. "Yes, my fault, but . . ." and he understood at last what Fix had done. "If I see him again, I'll kill him!" he decided.

Passepartout was on his way to Japan. He could not change that. "What shall I do when I arrive?" he asked himself. "My pockets are empty – not a penny. Everything is paid for on the ship – but after that . . .?" He decided to eat, because he would not be able to buy food in Japan.

He ate the food that he had paid for – for himself, for Phileas Fogg, for Aouda. He ate and ate.

On 13th November, the *Carnatic* sailed into the port of Yokohama.

Chapter 9
To San Francisco

Near Shanghai, the steamship *General Grant* had seen the little pilot-boat with her flag upside down. The American ship's captain ordered a change of direction. A few minutes later, Phileas Fogg had paid for the voyage to San Francisco. He had put five hundred and fifty pounds in Bunsby's pocket. And he and Aouda and Fix were on board the ship.

When the *General Grant* arrived in Yokohama on the morning of 14th November, Fogg and Aouda went straight to the *Carnatic*. They learnt that Passepartout had arrived the day before. Aouda was very glad – and perhaps Fogg was, too, but nobody could see that.

Then they started looking and asking questions everywhere, trying to find him. The *General Grant* was going to sail that evening for San Francisco. It was by chance – or perhaps by one of those strange feelings that lead one to something – that they went through a garden where Passepartout was sitting in the sun, trying to think what to do. He was very pleased to see them again and they all went quickly to the *General Grant*.

In Yokohama, Fix went to the office of the British consul. The warrant was there – too late because Fogg had left British lands, and the warrant was useless in Japan or the United States. Fix had to travel back, with the warrant, to England.

Passepartout saw Fix on the ship the next day, and the Frenchman attacked the detective. When Fix was down on his back, Passepartout was pleased – and less angry.

"Have you finished?" asked Fix.

"Yes, for the moment."

"Well, come and let's have a talk."

"A talk?"

"Yes. To help your employer. I'm on your side now."

"Oh!" said Passepartout. "So at last you know that my employer is not a thief."

"No. I still think he's a thief, and I have a warrant for his arrest——" He saw Passepartout was going to hit him again, and he went on quickly: "I can't use the warrant here. Mr Fogg seems to be going to England, and I can use it there. So I want to help him to get to England as quickly as possible. That's what you want too. So we're on the same side. We can be friends."

"Friends? Never!" said Passepartout. "But we can work together to help my employer."

The *General Grant* travelled fast, using her sails as well as her engine. On 3rd December, she sailed through the Golden Gate into San Francisco.

The General Grant *sails into San Francisco*

Chapter 10
Across America

The train for New York was to leave at 6 o'clock in the evening.

After lunch, Phileas Fogg went with Aouda to get a stamp in his passport. On the way out of the hotel, Passepartout asked about buying guns for the railway journey. He had heard about attacks on the trains by Sioux and Pawnee Indians. Fogg did not think it was useful to have a lot of guns, but he told Passepartout to do as he pleased.

At 5.45, Phileas Fogg, Aouda and Passepartout were at the station, where the train was ready to start. Passepartout had bought six Colt revolvers.

Mr Fogg was surprised to see Fix at the station, too.

In the old days, it took six months or more to make the journey between San Francisco and New York. Now, with the railway, the time was seven days. Phileas Fogg expected to reach New York in time to get the ship for Liverpool on 11th December.

The first unexpected stop came after the train had reached the great open grasslands of the prairies. For hours, the travellers had seen great numbers of bison – the Americans called them buffaloes. They knew that great armies of these buffaloes – thousands of them – crossed the railway line. Then the trains had to stop and wait until the line was clear.

It happened at about 3 o'clock in the afternoon. There were ten or twelve thousand of the great beasts in front of the train. The driver tried to push them out of the way with the "cowcatcher" in front of the engine. But the great crowd of animals could not be moved.

The passengers watched the beasts slowly moving past the train. The only passenger who seemed not to mind the delay was Phileas Fogg. Passepartout was very angry with the buffaloes. He wanted to shoot them with all his revolvers, but that would have been useless. It took three hours for the great crowd of buffaloes to move slowly across and leave the line clear.

Phileas Fogg was playing whist with Aouda and Fix when the next unexpected stop came.

"It's a bridge," said a railwayman. "The bridge over the river at Medicine Bow is broken. It still has the railway line over it, but this heavy train would finish it. The passengers must walk twenty kilometres to the next station beyond the bridge. They will have to wait there – about six hours – for another train."

The passengers, except Phileas Fogg, looked very unhappy.

At that moment, the driver came along the train.

The driver tries to move the buffaloes with the "cowcatcher"

"Gentlemen," he said. "There may be a way of getting over. If we cross as fast as possible, we may be all right."

The passengers liked that.

The driver went back to his engine. He drove the train back for a few kilometres. Then he and his fireman built up the fire, and the driver started. The train went forwards again, faster – and faster. They were travelling at one hundred and sixty kilometres an hour. The sound coming from the engine was one loud hiss, as they reached the bridge. The whole train seemed to throw itself from one river bank to the other. They were across!

The great noise behind them meant that the whole bridge had fallen into the river fifty metres below. But they did not see it. The driver could not stop the train until it had run twenty kilometres along the line.

It was the next morning that the passengers heard cries, shouts, shots – all the sounds of battle. A party of Sioux had attacked the train to kill and steal.

The passengers, with their revolvers, fought back. The Sioux had made attacks like this before. They did not wait for the train to stop, but climbed into the carriages from each end – a hundred or more of them. They had guns, and the noise of their shots and the revolver shots of the passengers was frightening.

The train ran on. A small party of the Sioux had climbed from their horses on to the engine. They had attacked and half-killed the driver and his fireman. One Sioux chief tried to stop the train, but he did not understand the engine. The train went faster instead of slower.

They were less than four kilometres from the station at Fort Kearney, where there were soldiers. If they could stop near the station, the passengers would be saved. If not ...

Passepartout called out: "I'll go." And he climbed over the end of the carriage, where the Sioux could not see him. Then the brave young man made his way from hand-hold to hand-hold under the carriages until he reached the front of the train. The engine was joined to the carriages by heavy couplings. Passepartout had to wait until a movement of the train made it possible to move each coupling. But at last the carriages were separated from the engine. The engine ran on, faster and faster. The carriages ran on, but more slowly, until they stopped quite near to Fort Kearney.

The soldiers heard the shooting and ran out. The Sioux had not expected them. Those Indians who were alive escaped.

The passengers who were unhurt walked to the station, carrying the badly wounded. There they counted their numbers.

Passepartout was one of three passengers who had been taken away by the Sioux. Aouda was in tears, but Fogg said to her: "I'll get him back."

The captain of the soldiers chose thirty men to go with Phileas Fogg. The rest had to stay at Fort Kearney to guard the fort and the station.

Fix wondered what to do. He wanted to go with Fogg, but Fogg said, "Please stay here and guard the lady."

Aouda saw Fogg walk away. It was snowing, and the little party soon disappeared. The young lady's eyes were wet with tears. Not only was Passepartout gone and in danger, but Phileas Fogg had gone too – gone to put his own life in danger, throwing away all chance of winning his bet.

More and more snow fell out of a dark sky.

In the afternoon, an engine arrived from the east. It was the engine from their own train. It had run on until the fire died down and it slowly came to a stop. The driver and fireman were not dead. After a long time, they sat up and understood what had happened.

"We must go back," the driver said. "They're in trouble back there."

At Fort Kearney, they joined the carriages to the engine, and then they told the passengers to get into the train.

"Can't you wait?" asked Aouda. And she told the railwaymen about Phileas Fogg, Passepartout, and the two other passengers.

But they could not wait. "We're very late already," they said. "Please get into the train."

"No," said Aouda. "I'll stay here."

Fix stayed with her, and they watched the train move away into the falling snow.

Phileas Fogg and the thirty soldiers did not come back that day or during the night that followed. In the morning, the captain was wondering what to do, and Aouda was nearly crying again, when they heard a shout. The small group appeared, with Phileas Fogg, Passepartout, and the two other passengers walking with the soldiers.

There had been a fight. But the Sioux had soon run away, leaving some of their number on the ground. Passepartout himself had dealt with some of them, striking them with his hands and feet.

"Where's the train?" asked Passepartout.

"Gone!" said Fix.

"And the next train?" Phileas Fogg wanted to know.

"Not until this evening."

"I see," said Fogg. That train would arrive too late in New York. He was twenty hours behind his timetable, but he said nothing about that.

Their train arrived in New York at 11.15 in the evening. The Cunard line ship *China* had sailed for Liverpool at 10.30!

Chapter 11
Across the Atlantic

It seemed that Phileas Fogg had lost his bet. None of the other shipping lines – the White Star line, the French line, the Hamburg–America line, and others – had sailings that would get him to London by 21st December.

Phileas Fogg took Aouda to a hotel, and then went to the Hudson River to try to find a ship. There were a lot of sailing ships, but no sailing ship could cross the Atlantic quickly enough.

At last he saw a ship that looked fast. She had sails as well as an engine. Fogg saw smoke coming from it, as if it was getting ready to leave. He went to it. It was a strong-looking ship, with iron bottom and sides, but with all the cabins and top parts of wood.

Phileas Fogg went on board and spoke to the captain: "Are you sailing soon, captain?"

"In an hour," said the captain. He was a hard man, and his answer was unfriendly.

"Where are you going?"

"To Bordeaux."

"Are you taking passengers?"

"Never."

"Is she a fast ship?" asked Fogg.

"Yes. The *Henrietta* is well known. She does twenty-two kilometres an hour at least. Ask anyone. My name is Speedy."

"Will you take me, and three others, to Liverpool, Captain Speedy?"

"No!"

"The owners might be willing?"

"*I* am the owner."

"Then I'll buy the ship from you."

"No!"

Phileas Fogg thought for a minute. Then he said: "Will you take us to Bordeaux?"

"No! Not even if you paid me two hundred dollars."

"I offer you two thousand dollars."

"Each?"

"Each."

Captain Speedy thought. He could get eight thousand dollars without changing the voyage.

"We sail at nine," he said.

Fogg went quickly to the hotel and came back with Aouda, Passepartout, and even Fix, who gladly took Fogg's offer of a voyage to Europe. They were on board the ship when she sailed at 9 o'clock.

The next day, 13th December, a man went up to the *Henrietta*'s bridge to find the sun's height at 12 midday. You might think it would be Captain Speedy. It was not. The man on the bridge was Phileas Fogg.

Captain Speedy was locked in his cabin. He was making very loud angry noises in it.

What had happened? Phileas Fogg wanted

to go to Liverpool. The captain would not take him there. But the rest of the ship's officers and men, who hated the captain, wanted to take the four passengers to Liverpool. Some large presents of banknotes caused them to decide to help Phileas Fogg. And that is why the captain was locked in his cabin. Aouda was not very happy about it; Fix did not know what to think; Passepartout thought it was quite wonderful, and great fun.

It was quite clear that Phileas Fogg had once been a sailor. With the engine at its fastest, and with sails to help her, the *Henrietta* travelled quickly over the water.

They had done nearly half the crossing when the chief engineer spoke to Fogg:

"We had enough coal for a voyage at half-speed to Bordeaux. But we have been going at full speed and using a lot of coal. There isn't enough coal to take us at this speed to Liverpool."

"Thank you," said Phileas Fogg. "I'll have to think about it." He walked round the ship, looking at all the cabins and other parts. Then he told the engineer: "Keep going at full speed until all the coal is used up." He called Passepartout. "Bring Captain Speedy to me."

Captain Speedy ran up to the bridge. He seemed to be ready to kill Phileas Fogg. "Thief!" he shouted. "Pirate! Where are we?"

"Four hundred and eighty kilometres from

Liverpool," said Fogg. "But I sent for you, captain, because I want you to sell me your ship."

"No! No! No!"

"You see, I have to burn it."

"Burn my ship!"

"Well, the top parts. We need the wood for the engine."

"My ship! A ship that cost fifty thousand dollars!"

"Here's sixty thousand," said Phileas Fogg, offering the captain a pile of banknotes.

"Oh!" Captain Speedy was suddenly a different man. It was true that the *Henrietta* cost fifty thousand dollars, but she was twenty years old. "The iron parts of the ship – I can keep them, can I?"

"Yes. And the engine."

"Thank you," said the captain. "And now, do you still want to reach Liverpool?"

"I want to get to London the quickest way," answered Phileas Fogg.

"Queenstown in Ireland is much nearer than Liverpool. Queenstown is where the fast Atlantic passenger ships leave the letters for London. The post goes by fast train to Dublin, then by fast ship to Liverpool."

That is how, at 11.40 on 21st December, Phileas Fogg put his foot on the ground in Liverpool. And at 11.41, Fix touched him on the shoulder and said: "Phileas Fogg, I arrest you in the name of the Queen."

Chapter 12
The end of the journey

Phileas Fogg was locked up in the police station. He wrote in his pocket-book:

21st December. Saturday. Liverpool. 80th day. 11.40 in the morning ...

He looked at his watch. Two o'clock. A very fast train could still take him to London in time to be at the Reform Club by 8.45.

At 2.33, there was a lot of noise in the police station. The door was opened, and Fix ran in. He was out of breath, red in the face.

"Sir ..." he cried, "Mr Fogg, sir ... forgive me ... a mistake ... so sorry! The real bank thief was arrested three days ago! Forgive ..."

Then Phileas Fogg made the only really quick movement of his life: he struck Fix – hard – with both hands. Fix fell on the floor and did not try to get up.

Passepartout had followed Fix. "Oh, well done, sir!" he cried.

Aouda was waiting at the police station. The three of them jumped into a carriage and drove to the Liverpool railway station.

The London train had left, half an hour before.

Phileas Fogg ordered a special train. He offered money freely, but there were delays. When the train reached the London station, the clock showed 8.50. Phileas Fogg had made his journey round the world, and he was five minutes late. He had lost.

Aouda and Passepartout seemed to feel much more strongly than Phileas Fogg the fact that he had lost. This fine man had spent nearly all the twenty thousand pounds that he had taken on the journey. He had another twenty thousand pounds in Baring's Bank, but now he had to pay all of it to the gentlemen in the Reform Club.

Phileas Fogg spent the next day looking at money matters and putting his life in order.

At half past seven in the evening, he came down and spoke to Aouda. He was as cool and unexcited as usual.

"Madam," he said, "can you forgive me for bringing you to England?"

"Can *I* forgive *you*?" She felt her heart beating strangely.

"Yes. When I decided to bring you here, I was rich. I expected to be able to give you a part of my riches. Then you could have had a pleasant life here, away from the danger from the prince's men in your own country. Now I am a poor man. I have very little money left, but I want to give it to you, if you will let me."

Aouda stood up.

"Can't we be poor together?" she asked. "I mean, won't you ask me to be your wife?" And she held her hand out to him.

Phileas Fogg could hardly look into the gentle eyes that told him of her simple love.

"You knew it?" he said. "You knew that I love you – with all my heart!"

The bell rang for Passepartout, and he came running. Mr Fogg still had Aouda's little hand in his. Passepartout saw that, and the joy shone in his face.

"Do you think, Passepartout," Phileas Fogg said, "that it is too late to speak to Mr Wilson, the priest in the church round the corner?"

Passepartout's smile grew wider. "Never too late," he said.

It was only 8.05.

"For tomorrow, Monday?" Passepartout asked.

"For tomorrow, Monday," said Phileas Fogg and Aouda together.

Passepartout went out, running.

The people of England had changed their minds twice about Phileas Fogg. First he was a brave sportsman who had made a bet that everyone hoped he would win. Then, because the papers said so, he was a bank thief, running away from the police. Now the real thief had been caught, and Fogg was again the wonderful sportsman.

There was a great crowd round the Reform Club on the Saturday evening when the people hoped to see him arrive.

Phileas Fogg's friends were playing whist in the Reform Club that evening.

When the clock showed 8.25, Stuart said: "In twenty minutes he'll be too late. The last train from Liverpool arrived at 7.23, and the next one doesn't arrive until 12.10. I'm afraid we've won our bet."

They played for some time in silence.

"Eight forty-three," said Stuart.

Two more minutes, and they would win their bet. They were none of them glad.

With five seconds to go before 8.45, a great noise was heard from outside the club – shouting, cheering, joyful cries.

With two seconds to go, the door opened. Phileas Fogg appeared. Quietly he said:

"Here I am, gentlemen."

Passepartout had run to the priest's house. Mr Wilson had not yet come home, and the Frenchman had to wait.

He waited at least twenty minutes. It was 8.35 when he came out of the priest's house. He had no hat, no coat. He was running. Running as if for his life. He could hardly speak when he reached the Savile Row house.

"What's the matter?" asked Phileas Fogg.

"Sir ... impossible ... marriage not possible ... not possible tomorrow. Tomorrow is Sunday ..."

"Monday," said Fogg.

Phileas Fogg comes into the Reform Club

"No ... today's Saturday ..."

"It can't be Saturday."

"Yes, it is!" cried Passepartout, who had got his breath back. "We made a mistake of one day. We arrived a day early. But there's only ten minutes left. Come on, sir!" He had hold of Fogg's coat, and he was pulling him to the door.

We know now that Fogg arrived just in time to win his bet. He had gone round the world in eighty days!

How was the mistake made? Fogg had gone *east* round the world, and so he had gained one day.

There was one thousand pounds left in the overnight bag. Phileas Fogg gave it to Passepartout.

Winning the bet had made Fogg a rich man again. Trying to let no feelings appear in his face or his voice, he asked Aouda:

"The marriage – do you still want to marry me?"

"Mr Fogg, *I* must ask that question. When I dared to speak about it, you were poor. Now you are rich——"

"Excuse me, madam. The money is yours. If you hadn't thought about the marriage, Passepartout wouldn't have gone to see Mr Wilson. If he hadn't spoken to Mr Wilson, I wouldn't have known about the mistake, and ..."

"Dear Mr Fogg!" laughed the young woman.

"Dear Aouda!" Phileas Fogg answered.

Questions

Questions on each chapter

1 *Phileas Fogg and Passepartout*
   1 Where did Phileas Fogg spend most of each day?
   2 What did Passepartout become on 2nd October 1872?
   3 When did Phileas Fogg go to bed every night?

2 *The bet*
   1 What card game did Phileas Fogg like?
   2 What did the papers say about the railway in India?
   3 What was Stuart's bet?
   4 When did Fogg expect to be back at the Reform Club?
   5 How much money did Fogg take with him?

3 *Detective Fix*
   1 Where did Fix first see Phileas Fogg?
   2 Why was Passepartout's watch wrong? (Because ...)
   3 Which passenger joined the ship at Suez?

4 *India*
   1 What did Fix hope to receive in Bombay?
   2 What happened to Passepartout's shoes?
   3 Why did the train stop at Kholby? (Because ...)
   4 What did Fogg pay for an elephant?

5 *Aouda*
   1 Where was the dead prince's body?
   2 What did Fogg do with the elephant?
   3 Why was Aouda glad to go to Hong Kong?

6 *Calcutta*
   1 Where had the priests come from?
   2 Who had brought them to Calcutta?
   3 How much bail did Fogg have to leave?

7 *To Hong Kong*
  1 Why was Fix on the *Rangoon*?
  2 Where did Fogg want to go on the *Carnatic*?
  3 Why did Fix look unhappy?
  4 What did Passepartout have to tell Fogg?
  5 What did Fix do to Passepartout's drink?

8 *To Japan*
  1 Why did the words "wait a week" make Fix happy?
  2 How much did Fogg offer the pilot?
  3 What fact was not in *Bradshaw*?
  4 Who sailed with Fogg and Aouda on the *Tankadere*?
  5 Why did the pilot-boat have to use only the smallest sail?
  6 What does it mean when a boat's flag is upside down?
  7 Where was Passepartout?

9 *To San Francisco*
  1 Where did Fogg find Passepartout?
  2 Why couldn't Fix arrest Fogg?
  3 What did Passepartout do when he saw Fix?

10 *Across America*
  1 What did Passepartout buy in San Francisco?
  2 What are the prairies?
  3 How long did the buffaloes delay the train?
  4 Where was the broken bridge?
  5 Who attacked the train?
  6 Who separated the engine from the carriages?
  7 Why did Phileas Fogg miss the Cunard ship?

11 *Across the Atlantic*
  1 Who was the captain of the *Henrietta*?
  2 Who was the man on the bridge on the second day?
  3 Why did Fogg want to burn parts of the ship?
  4 How much did the ship cost Phileas Fogg?
  5 What did Fix do in Liverpool?

12 *The end of the journey*
  1 What did Phileas Fogg do to Fix?
  2 At what time did Fogg's train reach London?
  3 Why was there a crowd round the Reform Club?
  4 At what time did Phileas Fogg appear in the club?
  5 What mistake did Phileas Fogg make? Why?

Questions on the whole story

These are harder questions. Read the Introduction, and think hard about the questions before you answer them. Some of them ask for your opinion, and there is no fixed answer.

1   a   In *The Times* timetable on page 5 there is a line: "*Bombay to Calcutta* – railway – 3 days". What was wrong with that?
    b   What happened to make "*San Francisco to New York* – railway – 7 days" wrong?
    c   What did Phileas Fogg have to do instead of "*Hong Kong to Yokohama* – ship"?

2   Do you like Fix, the detective? Can you give a reason for liking or disliking him?

3   Passepartout:
    a   Can you describe two brave things that he did?
    b   Sometimes Passepartout did foolish things that caused delay for Phileas Fogg. Can you name the foolish thing that he did at (i) Bombay, (ii) Hong Kong?
    c   What did Passepartout hope for when Phileas Fogg first became his employer?
    d   Near the end of the story we read, about Passepartout, that "the joy shone in his face" (page 51). Why?

4   Aouda:
    a   When does the reader first think she might be in love with Phileas Fogg?
    b   When does the reader first think Phileas Fogg might be in love with her?
    c   Give one example that shows that Aouda was brave.

5   Phileas Fogg:
    a   At the beginning, Phileas Fogg is "a clock" (page 2). What did Passepartout mean?
    b   Do you think Fogg changed during the journey? Give examples.
    c   Did Fogg himself change, or did Passepartout's understanding of him change? Give a reason for your opinion.

6   Do you find it hard to believe the story in places? Give examples.

New words

arrest
stop (a person) and take him or her to a police station

bail
money left with a court of law so that a person may be set free until he or she is tried. If the person does not come back, the money is lost.

bet
offer to pay money to somebody if the result of a certain happening is not what you expect. If what you expect is right, he or she will pay you.

cabin
a small bedroom on a ship

coupling
a metal thing that joins one part of a train to another

delay
cause something or somebody to be late; being late

engine
a machine that drives a ship through the water; a machine on wheels that pulls a railway train;

engineer = a person who drives or looks after an engine

guard
keep (a person or place) safe

pilot
a seaman who knows the way into a port and can take ships into it. In the old days, pilots like Bunsby in this story went out in their **pilot-boats** to meet arriving ships. The first to reach the ship usually became its **pilot**.

priest
a man who works in a church or temple and leads the people who come to it

temple
a building in which prayers are said to a god or gods

voyage
a journey by sea

warrant
a paper from a judge which allows the police to do something or **arrest** someone

willingly
wanting to (do something)